PIANO/VOCAL/CHORDS

MOVIE SHEET MUSIC HITS

Published 2004

© International Music Publications Ltd
Griffin House 161 Hammersmith Road London W6 8BS England

Editorial management: Artemis Music Limited (www.artemismusic.com)

Across The Stars (from *Star Wars: Episode II - Attack Of The Clones*)

Music by John Williams

Moderately slow & gently (♩ = 76)

Appassionato

Because You Loved Me
(from *Upclose And Personal*)

Words and Music by Diane Warren

And All That Jazz
(from *Chicago*)

Words by John Kander
Music by Fred Ebb

Come on, babe,— why don't we paint the town,— And all that jazz!— I'm gon-na rouge my knees— and roll my stock-ings down—

And all that jazz!— Start the car,— I know a whoop-ee spot— where the

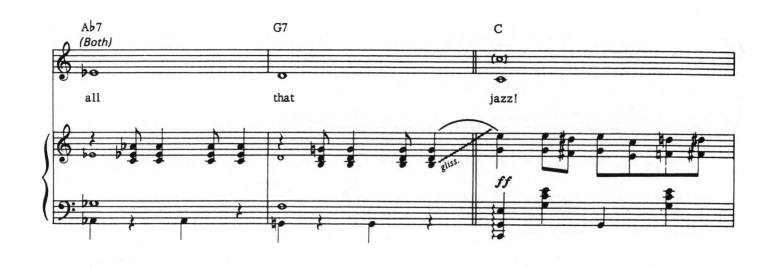

all   that   jazz!

Arthur's Theme
(Best That You Can Do) (from *Arthur*)

Words and Music Peter Allen, Burt Bacharach, Christopher Cross and Carole Bayer-Sager

As Time Goes By
(from *Casablanca*)

Words and Music by Herman Hupfeld

Come What May
(from *Moulin Rouge*)

Words and Music by David Baerwald and Kevin Gilbert

Chorus:

Eye Of The Tiger
(from *Rocky III*)

Words and Music by James Peterik and Frank Sullivan

Repeat and fade

The eye of the ti - ger.

The eye of the ti -

The Entertainer
(from *The Sting*)

Music by Scott Joplin

41

Fawkes The Phoenix (from
Harry Potter & The Chamber Of Secrets)

Music by John Williams

Gollum's Song (from
The Lord Of The Rings: The Two Towers)

Words by Fran Walsh
Music by Howard Shore

Hedwig's Theme (from
Harry Potter & The Philosopher's Stone)

Music by John Williams

(with pedal)

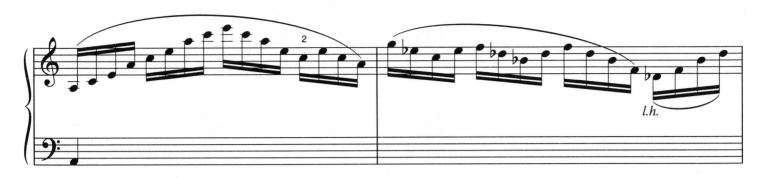

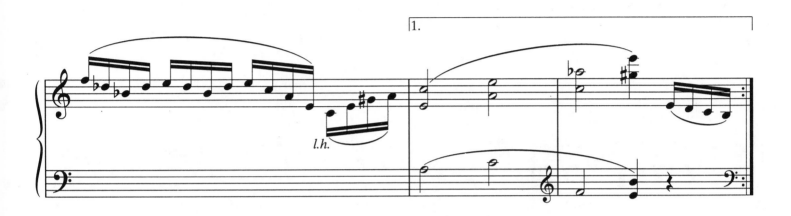

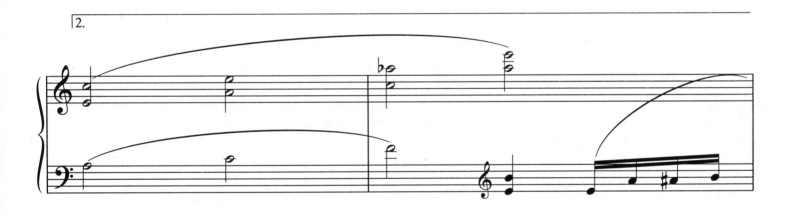

How Do I Live
(from *Con Air*)

Words and Music by Diane Warren

1. How do I _____ get through one night with-out__ you._____ If I had to

2. *See additional lyrics*

live with-out__ you,__ what kind of life would that be?___ Oh,__ I,_____ I need you in my

arms, need you__ to hold.___ You're my world, my heart,__ my soul.___ If you ev - er leave,__

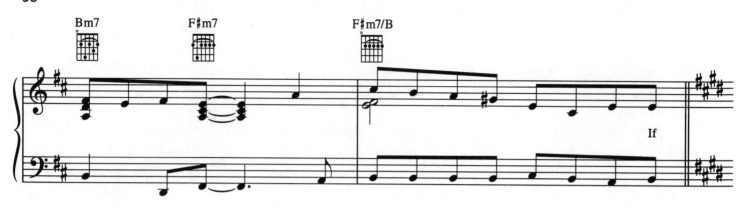

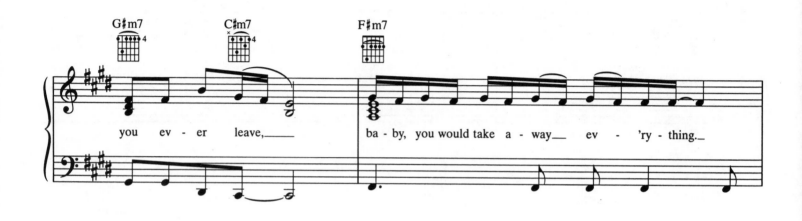

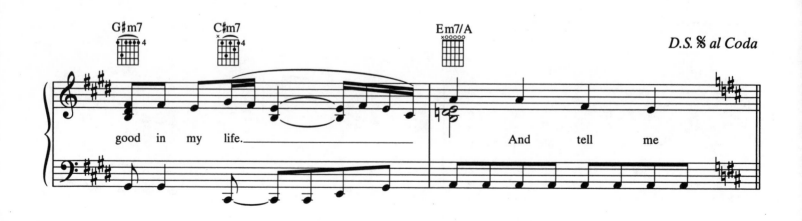

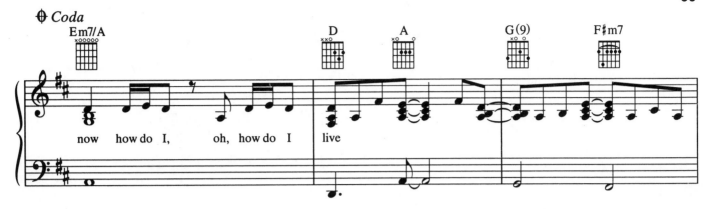

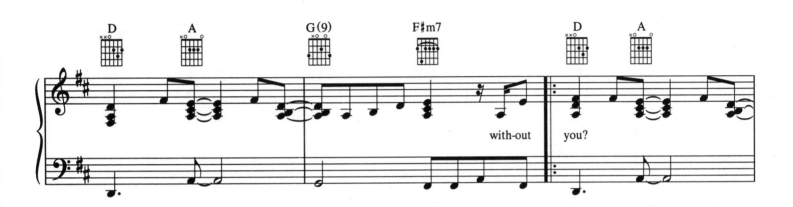

Repeat ad lib. and fade
(vocal 1st time only)

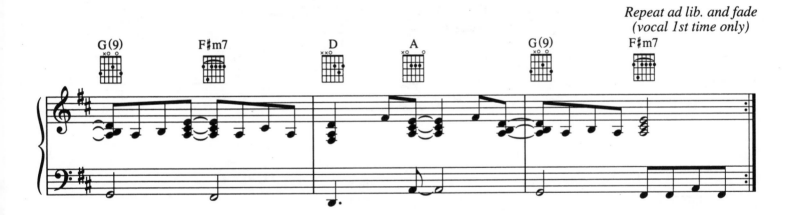

Verse 2:
Without you, there'd be no sun in my sky,
There would be no love in my life,
There'd be no world left for me.
And I, baby, I don't know what I would do,
I'd be lost if I lost you.
If you ever leave,
Baby, you would take away everything real in my life.
And tell me now...
(To Chorus:)

I Don't Want To Miss A Thing
(from *Armageddon*)

Words and Music by Diane Warren

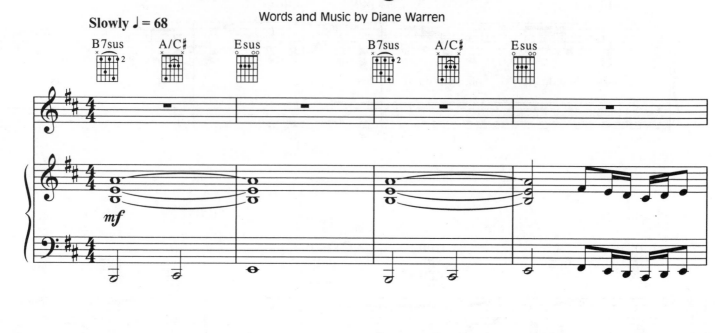

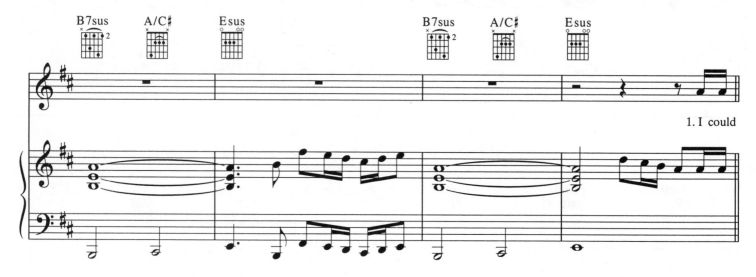

1. I could

Verse 1:

stay a-wake_ just to hear you breath - ing, watch you

G
D/F♯
Em7
smile while you are sleep - ing, while you're far a - way and dream - ing. I could
D
A/C♯
Bm7
G
D/F♯
spend my life in this sweet sur - ren - der. I could stay lost in this mo-ment for -
Em7
F♯m7
Gmaj7
Asus
ev - er. Ev-'ry mo-ment spent with you is a mo-ment I treas - ure.
Chorus:
D
A/C♯
Em7
Don't wan - na close my eyes, don't wan - na fall a - sleep, 'coz I'd

miss you, ba - by, and I don't wan-na miss a thing.___ 'Coz e - ven when I dream of you,___

the sweet-est dream would nev - er do.___ I'd still miss you, ba - by, and I don't wan-na miss a thing.___

Repeat ad lib. and fade

In Dreams (from *The Lord Of The Rings: The Fellowship Of The Ring*)

Words by Fran Walsh
Music by Howard Shore

I Move On
(from *Chicago*)

Words by Fred Ebb
Music by John Kander

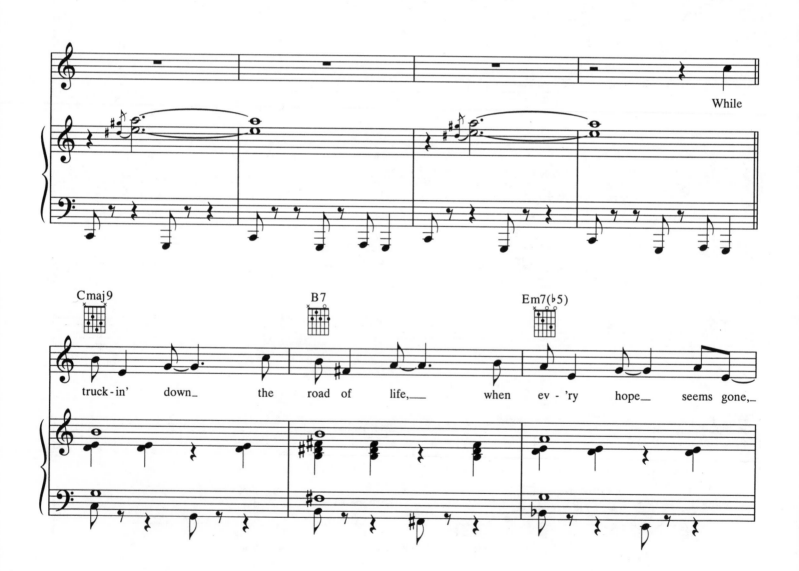

truck-in' down__ the road of life,__ when ev-'ry hope__ seems gone,__

While

Into The West (from *The Lord Of The Rings: The Return Of The King*)

Words and Music by Howard Shore, Fran Walsh and Annie Lennox

Moderately ♩ = 92

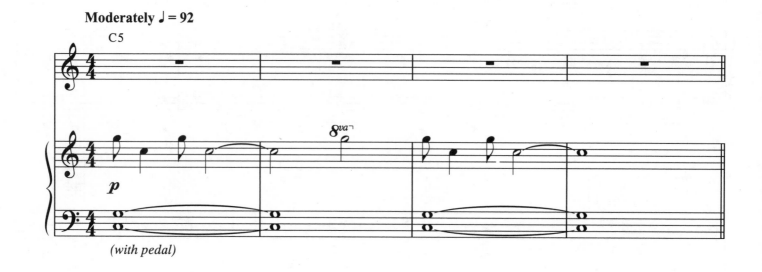

(with pedal)

Verse 1:

1. Lay____ down____ your sweet and wea-ry head.

Night is fall-ing.____ You have come to jour-ney's end.

It Might Be You
(from *Tootsie*)

Words by Alan Bergman and Marilyn Bergman
Music by Dave Grusin

87

James Bond Theme

Music by Monty Norman

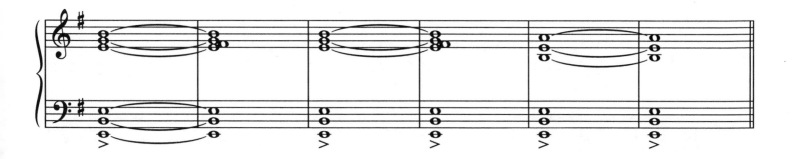

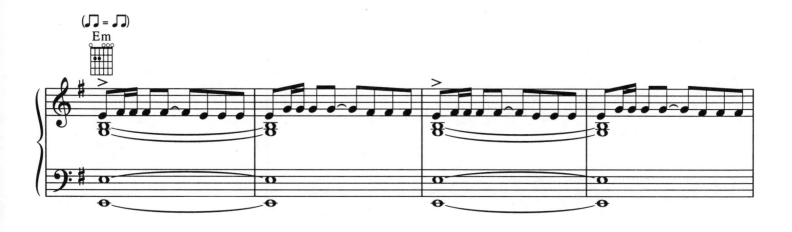

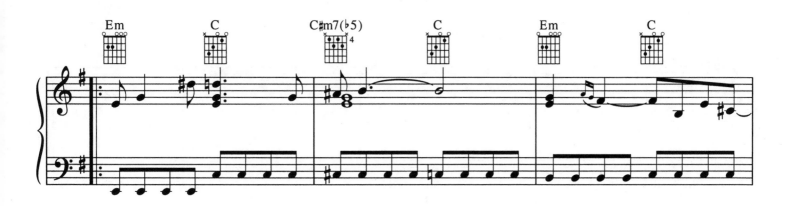

The Power Of Love
(from *Back To The Future*)

Words and Music by Chris Hayes, Huey Lewis and John Colla

The pow-er of love__ is a cu-ri-ous thing;

You feel the pow - er of love.

You feel the pow - er of love.

Feel the pow - er of love.

Repeat and fade

My Heart Will Go On
(from *Titanic*)

Words by Will Jennings
Music by James Horner

Over The Rainbow
(from *The Wizard Of Oz*)

Words by E Y Harburg
Music by Harold Arlen

Somewhere My Love (Lara's Theme)
(from *Doctor Zhivago*)

Words by Paul Francis Webster
Music by Maurice Jarre

Stayin' Alive
(from *Staying Alive*)

Words and Music by Barry Gibb, Robin Gibb and Maurice Gibb

That's What Friends Are For
(from *Night Shift*)

Words and Music by Burt Bacharach and Carole Bayer-Sager

There You'll Be
(from *Pearl Harbor*)

Words and Music by Diane Warren

The Wind Beneath My Wings
(from *Beaches*)

Words and Music by Larry Henley and Jeff Silbar

It must have been cold___ there___ in my shad - ow,

to nev - er have sun - light on your face.

You've been con - tent___ to let me shine,

Smash!

Alphabetical Songfinder